Performance Assessment Activities and Rubrics

GLENCOE
McGraw-Hill
New York, New York Columbus, Ohio Chicago, Illinois Peoria, Illinois Woodland Hills, California

To the Teacher

The American Republic to 1877 Performance Assessment Activities and Rubrics booklet provides activities for students to assemble samples of work for their portfolios. Guidelines and rubrics for teacher and student assessment are also provided. The first several pages of the booklet provide teacher information on using and evaluating performance assessment tasks.

Glencoe/McGraw-Hill

A Division of The ***McGraw-Hill*** *Companies*

Send all inquiries to:
Glencoe/McGraw-Hill
8787 Orion Place
Columbus, Ohio 43240

ISBN 0-07-829147-X

Printed in the United States of America

1 2 3 4 5 066 06 05 04 03 02

Table of Contents

Performance Task Assessment Lists and Scoring Rubrics

Defining Performance Assessment

Performance assessment is not simply a testing strategy, but a way of teaching and learning that integrates process and product. Effective teaching, meaningful learning, and motivation all play a role in planning and carrying out performance assessment. As students participate in performance assessment tasks, they are actively learning as well as evaluating their progress. The performance assessment activities in this book combine historical information and concepts with interdisciplinary tasks. Each performance task involves students in developing processes and crafting products for specific audiences.

PERFORMANCE ASSESSMENT LOOKS AT AUTHENTIC USE OF INFORMATION

A common model of assessment is to teach the chapter, then stop, and test the students. Performance assessment changes this pattern. With performance assessment, *The American Republic to 1877* becomes a learning resource—a means to an end rather than the end in itself.

When students leave school, they will use books and other sources to find information on a variety of subjects. Performance assessment tasks all use information as it is used in the larger world. Schoolwork becomes valid preparation for life outside the classroom. The teacher guides a student's efforts, provides models of excellent work, and gives feedback each step of the way. The following flow chart illustrates the process for information problem solving.

Information Problem Solving

Finding and Using Information

Ask Questions

Understand the Task

- Select a reasonable and focused topic.
- Know the purpose of the product.
- Understand how the product will be presented.
- Identify the audience for the product.

Survey Existing Knowledge and Prepare for New Learning

- Summarize what is known.
- Outline what needs to be learned.
- Identify information sources.
- Prepare a task/time management plan.

Research the Selected Topic

- Use a variety of quality information sources.
- Collect and organize information.

Construct a Product

- Writing
  - Reports
  - Journal Entries
  - Articles
  - Song Lyrics
  - Scripts
- Oral Presentation
  - Role Plays
- Visual Presentation
  - Drawings/Posters
  - Models
  - Bulletin Boards
  - Maps
  - Graphs
  - Graphic Organizers

Assess the Whole Process

- Identify strengths and weaknesses of the process.
- Identify strengths and weaknesses of the final product.
- List goals to improve future work.

★ Performance Assessment Activities and Rubrics

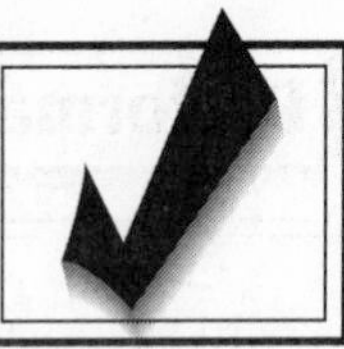

PERFORMANCE ASSESSMENT TASKS REQUIRE THINKING SKILLS

Thinking skills provide the "verbs" that direct the action in performance assessment tasks. The tasks involve:

- **Getting the information** (finding, collecting, reading, listening, observing).
- **Working with the information** (comparing, contrasting, classifying, inferring, analyzing, synthesizing, generalizing, evaluating, making models, or reasoning).
- **Using the information for a purpose** (informing, persuading, motivating).
- **Using information to craft a product/ presentation** (speaking, writing, designing, constructing, demonstrating).
- **Using information to communicate with specific audiences** (peers, younger, older, informed, diverse groups).

PERFORMANCE ASSESSMENT INVOLVES COOPERATIVE LEARNING

Cooperative learning is a valuable skill in the larger world. Businesses seek employees who establish and maintain positive working relationships with others. Cooperative learning simulates this business environment. Performance assessment often uses a combination of individual and group learning activities. Group work in the initial step actively involves students and stimulates them to share ideas. When groups complete the entire project, individuals should be accountable for specific tasks, and each student should assess his or her own work. There is no group grade. (See Scoring Rubric: A Cooperative Group Management Plan and corresponding Performance Task Assessment List on pages 47 and 48.)

THE PERFORMANCE ASSESSMENT SYSTEM

Each part of the performance assessment system has a specific function. The central task requires the use of information, concepts, skills, and attitudes. The scoring rubrics and performance task assessment lists guide and evaluate the process and product. The models of excellent student work provide clear targets of quality and help students work independently. The entire system serves as an evaluation tool for the teacher.

The Performance Task

For each chapter in *The American Republic to 1877*, you will discover an activity featuring performance tasks. Use them as suggested, or change them to meet the individual needs of your students.

FORMAT OF A TASK

The first step in creating a performance assessment task is to identify the main concepts and thinking skills that you want to be the targets of the assessment. You may not give the task a title until later. In a few words state the background of the concept being addressed (e.g., establishing a democratic government). Next consider what type of product you want students to make. You may give students options or let them select the format for the product. The audience, also, may be decided by the students, or you may select one for them. Once students know the product and the audience, help them identify the product's purpose. Will it inform, persuade, or motivate the audience?

The next step involves writing the procedures. First, you may want to set the scene by giving the students some background. (Refer to pages 8 through 26 for some examples.) The directions can be very specific or very general depending on the degree of structure students need.

Finally, give the students some guidelines about the assessment. Explain that they will use performance task assessment lists and that the teacher will keep the grades and other official information. The students should keep a log of the tasks they complete.

INDIVIDUAL LOG

If students have the freedom to choose the task, purpose, or the audience, they should keep these individual records of tasks they need to accomplish. Students should mark the tasks they choose to save in a working folder so they can easily locate them when they make the final selections for their portfolios. Information in a student's log should include name, task title, type of product, audience for the task, purpose of the task, date completed, and overall self-assessment.

INDIVIDUAL TASK MANAGEMENT PLAN

Because students may lack experience with projects like performance assessment tasks, the individual performance task management plan helps students approach the task in an organized, thoughtful way. Checkpoints with due dates help assure that students carry out the plan according to schedule. Teachers provide these.

Finally, students need to identify problems or barriers to completion and consider solutions. When the plan is well done and complete, the student and teacher (and, in some cases, the parents) sign it. The Performance Task Assessment List for an Individual Performance Task Management Plan is located on page 50; the corresponding scoring rubric can be found on page 49.

Using Performance Assessment Tasks

The tasks in this book may be easily adapted by changing the product, purpose, or audience. Find audiences for the products and performances of your students. Audiences can include other students, citizens in the community, and parents and other adults. Involving outside audiences adds authenticity to the students' work.

USE A MIX OF ASSESSMENT STRATEGIES

Use quizzes, open-book exams, traditional tests, and performance assessment tasks in a combination that will allow you to evaluate how literate in American history your students are becoming.

START SLOWLY AND GO ONE STEP AT A TIME

You may begin by choosing just one performance assessment task. After some experience, you may want to add others. Another strategy is to give the students a menu of performance tasks early in the course, and allow the students to select one or two to complete as major projects for the course. At set times in the course, students present their products or performances to the class. If the students' tasks call for an outside audience, allow that experience to occur first. When a student reports to his or her peers in history class, the experience with the outside audience can be part of the report. Focus on how the performance tasks help build American history literacy in the students.

USE PERFORMANCE TASK ASSESSMENT LISTS AND MODELS OF EXCELLENT WORK

At the beginning of a performance task, show students the relevant performance task assessment list. Also show them examples of excellent work similar, but not identical, to their current project. If you do not have models of excellent work available at first, you and your colleagues can define criteria for excellent work in this course.

Students in subsequent classes will learn to use both the performance task assessment lists and the examples of excellent work from previous students to guide their work. As students create new examples of excellent products, you can add them to or substitute them for others in a set of benchmarks.

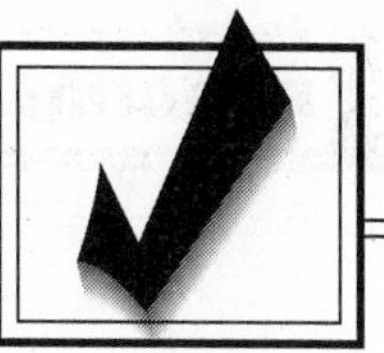

HELPING STUDENTS BECOME BETTER AT SELF-ASSESSMENT

If the students are not experienced in self-assessments, they will need training. After students complete tasks, ask them to respond to the following questions so they will gain experience with self-assessment.

1. What do you like most about your (product)? Why?
2. What was the most difficult part about making the (product)? Why?
3. If you were to do this project again, what would you do differently? Why?
4. If you were to revise this project one more time, how would you change it and why?
5. How did you craft your project so that it would be just right for the (specific audience)?
6. Describe a situation when you got stuck and were frustrated with the project. What helped you get going again?
7. What helps you be creative?
8. What are three words that describe you as a student? Explain how those three words best describe you.
9. If a camera were to take pictures of you working on this project, what would it see?
10. Who was the biggest help to you on this project? How did they help you?
11. How does this project show you that you really understand the concepts of American history?
12. How does this project show that you are making decisions to improve your understanding of American history?

Assessing Tasks

Focus student attention on how the performance tasks help build American history literacy using scoring rubrics and performance task assessment lists.

SCORING RUBRICS

A scoring rubric is a set of guidelines for assessing the quality of a process and / or product. The rubric includes a continuum of quality from excellent to poor. There are many varieties of rubrics. The one used in this book is a six-level rubric, known as the "two-decision rubric."

USING THE SCORING RUBRIC

To use the scoring rubric, the teacher studies the product and makes the first of two decisions. Is the product more like one that is excellent (**T**) or more like one that is poor (**W**)? If the product is more like a **T**, then the teacher makes the second and final decision. Is the product unusually excellent (**S**), evenly excellent (**T**), or mostly excellent (**U**)?

If the first decision is that the product is more like a **W**, then the teacher decides whether the product is evenly poor (**W**), mostly poor but with some better elements (**V**), or not done or very poorly done (**X**). After just two decisions, the teacher places the product on a six-point scale:

S Superb, eloquent, unusually excellent

T Evenly excellent

U Unevenly excellent, one or two important elements are not excellent

V Better than poor, one or two important elements are better than poor

W Evenly poor

X Not done or very poorly done

★ Performance Assessment Activities and Rubrics

Scoring rubrics in this book use letters instead of numerals so that teachers are not tempted to average the scores. The scores of 1, 2, 3, and 4 do represent a continuum of quality, but the degree of difference between each of the numbers is equal. Scoring rubrics are more like Continuum B than Continuum A in the following illustration. Adding these unequal values together to calculate a "mean" score is essentially meaningless.

Continuum A:

Equal intervals between values:

1 2 3 4

Continuum B:

Unequal intervals between values:

1 2 3 4 5 6

Consider the ratings made by this student on seven posters done throughout the course:

W U T U U T T

It would be correct to describe the student's long-term performance by reporting that he or she made three **T**s, three **U**s, and a **W**. The **T** ratings at the end show that the student improved with time and practice.

If two or more teachers evaluate the same performance or product, such as a poster, then using the same scoring rubric will help them both view it in the same way. Once a rubric has been created, many teachers can use it unaltered.

PERFORMANCE TASK ASSESSMENT LISTS

Teachers devise performance task assessment lists as guidelines for students. With experience, students working individually or in groups can make their own assessment lists—a measure that involves them more actively in their own learning.

STUDENTS' SELF-ASSESSMENT

The ability to self-assess and plan for improvement is a valuable life skill that performance assessment fosters. Students evaluate their work, identifying parts that are done well and those that need improvement. They use performance task instructions, the performance task assessment list, and the models of excellence as tools to improve their work.

AUDIENCE ASSESSMENT

Many of the performance tasks target an audience other than the classroom teacher. If possible, the audience should give the author feedback.

The Portfolio

Portfolios are a good way to look at a student's overall work. Take care not to just collect items, place them in a folder, and call it a portfolio. Plan portfolios with student benefits as the major consideration. One strategy is to have students save a variety of their best works. Near the end of the course, the teacher asks the students to select a small number of products that contributed to their total American history literacy.

When the students have made their selections, they each write a narrative explaining why they chose those particular items and how these items demonstrate their understanding of American history. The teacher reads the students' narratives and writes short responses. The portfolio and student narrative figure significantly in a student's final grade. This portfolio strategy engages the student in decision making, promotes self-analysis, and requires a reasonable amount of work from the teacher.

If you plan to use the portfolio, explain this assignment near the beginning of the course. Focus on the idea that the portfolio will be a small collection of a variety of items that will demonstrate how much the student has learned about American history.

★ DIFFICULT-TO-STORE PRODUCTS IN THE PORTFOLIO

Some items, such as written reports, journals, scripts, and booklets, will fit easily into a portfolio folder. Other items, such as posters and displays, may be too large or bulky. If possible students should keep photographs or videotapes of their very best works that do not fit into the portfolio. If this is not possible, then the student can refer to those products or performances only in the self-assessment narrative.

Grades

You may need to give students grades for their projects. On each performance task assessment list there is an opportunity for you to assign a point value to each element on the list. You and the student award points according to the quality of the work relevant to that element.

Using This Book

This booklet contains performance tasks for use with each of the 32 chapters in *The American Republic to 1877*. Note that the procedure found in each performance assessment refers students to particular task assessment lists. To guide you in your assessment of a task, use the corresponding rubric. A convenient list located near the top of each scoring rubric and performance task assessment list identifies particular performance assessment activities. You may wish to adapt the rubrics and assessment lists to meet your own needs.

Name ______________________ Date ______________ Class ________

★ Performance Assessment Activity 1

Use with Chapter 1

An Archaeological Exhibit

★ BACKGROUND

Archaeologists search for and examine fossil relics, monuments, and artifacts. Artifacts are characteristic products of a culture, including handmade objects such as tools and ornaments. Archaeologists continually find fascinating evidence about cultures that flourished in the Americas before the arrival of Europeans.

★ TASK

You and your friends are archaeologists. A museum curator has asked you to create a tabletop display showing the culture of one Native American nation. The exhibit will highlight fossil relics, artifacts, and monuments of this nation. Include models, drawings, and written explanations.

★ AUDIENCE

Your audience is museum visitors, including students and interested adults.

★ PURPOSE

The purpose of your exhibit is to help your audience visualize and understand daily life among the chosen Native American nation.

★ PROCEDURE

1. Consult the Performance Task Assessment Lists for a Model and a Cooperative Group Management Plan.
2. With your teammates decide upon a Native American group that will be the focus of your project.
3. Agree upon research, design, building, and drawing tasks for each member.
4. Complete your research. Share what you have learned with your teammates. Decide what elements to include in your exhibit.
5. Create a plan showing the location of each model artifact, fossil relic, and structure or drawing in your display. Choose your materials.
6. Together create the individual elements to include in your display.
7. With your teammates organize the elements to create a prototype (rough model) of your exhibit and write brief explanatory notes to accompany exhibit components, indicating their use or significance within the society.
8. Share your prototype with another group, obtain suggestions, and revise.
9. Create your final model exhibit.

★ ASSESSMENT

1. Use the performance task assessment lists suggested to evaluate your project.
2. Discuss what you might do differently if you do a similar project in the future.

Name ____________________ Date ____________ Class ________

★ Performance Assessment Activity 2

Use with Chapter 2

Sea Routes of Early Explorers

BACKGROUND

In the late 1400s European explorers searched for a sea route to Asia. One explorer, Christopher Columbus, sailed west. Columbus thought only water separated western Europe from eastern Asia. By accident he reached an unexpected treasure—the lands we now know as the Americas. Other explorers followed. The records of their voyages enlightened Europeans about the geographic features of the world.

TASK

You are a modern cartographer, or mapmaker. The publisher of an educational magazine has asked you to create a map to help modern students relate to the voyages of early European explorers. Your map will trace the route each took. Indicate modern reference points (bodies of water, cities, states, countries) that will help students recognize the sites early European explorers visited.

AUDIENCE

Young readers interested in learning more about the sites visited by early European explorers make up your audience.

PURPOSE

The purpose of your map is to help your audience understand and compare the routes taken and the sites visited by early European explorers.

PROCEDURE

1. Consult the Performance Task Assessment List for a Map as a guide.
2. Study various maps illustrating the travel routes and sites visited by early European explorers.
3. Using a ruler, establish a scale for your map.
4. Sketch an outline map of the world. Decide on color codes that will distinguish one explorer's voyage from another's expedition. Trace the routes taken by each explorer. Indicate the year(s) in which the voyage occurred.
5. Share your draft with a partner, get suggestions, and revise.
6. Create your final map. Add modern reference points that will help your readers relate the voyages to the world today.

ASSESSMENT

1. Use the Performance Task Assessment List for a Map to check your work as you progress toward your goals.
2. Add or improve elements at each stage as needed.
3. Your class can bind the maps to create a portfolio illustrating the expeditions of early European explorers.

Name ______________________ Date ______________ Class __________

★ Performance Assessment Activity 3

Use with Chapter 3

Hear Ye! Hear Ye! Read All About America!

BACKGROUND

English colonists began arriving in North America in the early 1600s. At this time the British often publicized information by distributing *broadsides,* which were advertisement or news items printed on one side of a large sheet of paper. Employees then *hawked* the broadside to the public. They sold it by hand in the street, while loudly proclaiming its contents.

TASK

You are a British publisher in the 1600s. A group that has obtained a charter to found a colony in North America approaches you for help. They want to recruit others to join in their venture. Your task is to create a poster (broadside) advertising their plans to found a British colony in North America.

AUDIENCE

Your audience is British citizens of the 1600s who might consider undertaking an expedition to colonize North America. Students, teachers, and other invited guests should play the roles of these British citizens.

PURPOSE

The purpose of your broadside is to persuade your audience that they should accompany your clients and help establish this colony.

PROCEDURE

1. Consult the Performance Task Assessment List for a Poster to guide you from initial planning to final display.
2. Research to discover more about broadsides and the people who might find this venture appealing.
3. Choose images to illustrate your message.
4. Draft an attention-getting slogan to accompany your artwork.
5. Design your poster.
6. Share your work with a partner to get feedback and suggestions for improvement. Revise as needed.
7. Create your final poster.

ASSESSMENT

1. Use the Performance Task Assessment List for a Poster when reviewing your work.
2. Add or improve elements at each stage as needed.
3. Complete a final self-assessment of your poster before displaying it.
4. Share your broadsides by "hawking" them in class.

Name ______________________ Date ______________ Class __________

★ Performance Assessment Activity 4

Use with Chapter 4

Establishing Rights and Obligations

BACKGROUND

European settlers arriving in the Americas established rules to govern their communities. When planning, they turned to the traditions of their homelands. For the British colonists, these customs included the concept of representative government and recognition of individual rights. The governments these early colonists founded laid the groundwork for our democratic institutions.

TASK

You and your friends plan to start a school community service club. Your task is to develop and write a charter, which defines the club's goals, establishes the rules for its operation, and explains the rights and duties of the officers and members.

AUDIENCE

Your audience is your teacher, classmates, and other students interested in joining your club.

PURPOSE

The purpose of your project is to help you understand the process involved in establishing a democratic organization.

PROCEDURE

1. Consult the Performance Task Assessment Lists for a Cooperative Group Management Plan and a Research Report as guides to assist you in planning, researching, and completing this project.
2. Research to find examples of charters for similar, established clubs.
3. Share what you discover with your teammates and together decide what elements you want to include in your charter.
4. As a team write a rough draft of your charter.
5. Share your work with another team for feedback and suggestions.
6. Revise to improve organization, clarity of detail, and precision of language.
7. Write and display the final draft of your charter. Be prepared to answer any questions others might have about plans for your organization.

ASSESSMENT

1. Use the performance task assessment lists suggested to check your work from the planning stages through final presentation.
2. Check to see that you have included all required elements in your charter.
3. Complete a final self-assessment before presenting your project.
4. You and your classmates might consider using the charters to establish a new school-based community service organization.

Name ______________________ Date ____________ Class ________

★ **Performance Assessment Activity 5**

Use with Chapter 5

Reporting from Lexington and Concord

BACKGROUND

By April 1775 armed conflict between Britain and the colonies seemed inevitable. Colonists everywhere anxiously discussed each new disagreement. Newspapers up and down the eastern seaboard rushed to print with news of the latest developments. In that year, two quiet Massachusetts villages gained instant fame as the first musket shots were heard. The names Lexington and Concord were on everyone's lips.

TASK

You are a reporter for a newspaper in one of the middle Atlantic or Southern colonies. Your editor has assigned you to write the story about the battles at Lexington and Concord. Include an attention-getting headline.

AUDIENCE

Your audience includes readers of your newspaper who are interested in the revolutionary developments of the colonial era.

PURPOSE

Your article is to inform your audience about the battles and their outcomes.

PROCEDURE

1. Consult the Performance Task Assessment Lists for a Newspaper Article and a Research Report.
2. Refer to the text and conduct further research to discover additional details about the battles.
3. Write a first draft and catchy title for your article.
4. Share your draft with a friend to obtain feedback and suggestions. Revise by adding accurate, vivid supporting details.
5. Check to see that you have included all elements. Prepare a final draft, adding and improving elements as necessary.

ASSESSMENT

1. Use the performance task assessment lists suggested to evaluate your newspaper article.
2. Check to see that you have included all elements.
3. Complete a final self-assessment of your work before you share it.

Name ______________________ Date ______________ Class ____________

★ Performance Assessment Activity 6

Use with Chapter 6

A Song of Victory

BACKGROUND

The British defeat at Yorktown had a terrible effect on Charles Cornwallis's troops. They never thought the ragtag colonial forces could rally and win the battle. Their disbelief showed when they surrendered their weapons to the Americans. A British army band played "The World Turned Upside Down." The title and lyrics reflected the mood of these soldiers.

TASK

You are a songwriter. A historical society is planning a musical play about the British surrender at Yorktown. Members have asked you to write an original song that George Washington's troops could have sung at this event.

AUDIENCE

Your audience is the viewers of the play.

PURPOSE

You will compose a song that captures the jubilant, victorious mood of the American troops.

PROCEDURE

1. Consult the Performance Task Assessment List for an Original Song to assist you in writing your song.
2. Research to learn more about the role music plays in rallying troops during war.
3. Find and study the lyrics of several patriotic songs popular during the Revolutionary War.
4. Write lyrics for your song, consulting a rhyming dictionary if necessary.
   a. Use words and phrases from your research.
   b. Create a lively phrase that can be repeated as a chorus.
5. Write a first draft of your song and exchange it with a partner to make suggestions, then revise and prepare a final copy of the song.
6. Perform your song for your classmates and teacher. Include an instrumental accompaniment if you wish.

ASSESSMENT

1. Use the Performance Task Assessment List for an Original Song to check your work.
2. Add or improve elements at each stage as needed.
3. Complete a final self-assessment of your song.

Name ______________________ Date ______________ Class ________

★ Performance Assessment Activity 7

Use with Chapter 7

The Art of Compromise

BACKGROUND

Representatives to the Constitutional Convention faced a difficult task. The country needed an effective central government. Delegates from states with smaller populations feared that states with larger populations might dominate a strong national government. The Framers of the Constitution had to create a government that did not overlook the interests of smaller states. A committee of delegates proposed the Great Compromise. Congress would have two houses. Each state would have equal representation in one of the houses. Population would determine the number of representatives in the other house.

TASK

You are a member of the committee that drafted the Great Compromise. The committee has asked you to address the convention. Your task is to write and present a speech explaining your proposal.

AUDIENCE

"Delegates to the Constitutional Convention" are your audience. Students, teachers, and other invited guests should act as these delegates.

PURPOSE

Your purpose is to persuade your audience that this compromise will ensure that both large and small states will have equal representation.

PROCEDURE

1. Consult the Performance Task Assessment Lists for an Oral Presentation and a Research Report.
2. Research to discover as much information as possible about the Great Compromise and the issues it addressed.
3. Using the information you have discovered, prepare note cards with specific details you will include in your oral presentation.
4. Design and create visual aids that will highlight your main points.
5. Practice your presentation and share your visual aids with a classmate for feedback and suggestions for improvement; then revise.
6. Give a formal presentation of your work to your audience.

ASSESSMENT

1. Use the performance task assessment lists suggested to check your work and add to or improve it as needed.
2. Think about what you might do to improve your delivery if you need to make a speech in the future.
3. Complete a final self-assessment of your entire project.

Name ____________________ Date ______________ Class __________

★ Performance Assessment Activity 8

Use with Chapter 8

An Architectural Exhibit

BACKGROUND

In 1800 John and Abigail Adams moved into a new gray limestone building. They became the first family to occupy the official home of the presidents. The building has undergone many additions and changes over the years. British troops burned the original structure during the War of 1812. Renovators used white paint to cover the smoke stains on the walls. We know this residence today as the White House.

TASK

You are an architect. The history department of a local university plans an exhibit about historic buildings. They have hired you to create a bulletin board display featuring the White House. Your task is to illustrate the changes that have been made to the original design.

AUDIENCE

Your audience is your teacher, classmates, and other students and adults interested in learning more about the history of the White House.

PURPOSE

Your purpose is to help your audience visualize the architectural development of the White House and to help them recognize when these changes occurred.

PROCEDURE

1. Consult the Performance Task Assessment Lists for a Bulletin Board Display and an Individual Performance Task Management Plan to assist you in planning and developing your project.
2. Research to learn as much as possible about the original design of the White House as well as what, when, and why structural changes occurred.
3. Locate magazine or newspaper pictures, photographs, or create original scale drawings of the original structure and subsequent additions.
4. Sketch ideas of what you will place on the bulletin board and how you will organize these materials.
5. Share your ideas with a classmate to obtain suggestions for improvement.
6. Revise your work as appropriate and create your final bulletin board display.

ASSESSMENT

1. Use the performance task assessment lists suggested to evaluate each stage of your bulletin board plan.
2. Check to see that you have included all elements.
3. Organize all the materials that you plan to put on your bulletin board.
4. Complete a final self-assessment before you share your project.

Name ______________________ Date ______________ Class __________

★ Performance Assessment Activity 9

Use with Chapter 9

A Jigsaw Puzzle Map

★ BACKGROUND

In 1803 President Thomas Jefferson offered to buy the city of New Orleans from France. To his shock, the French offered an additional 800,000 square miles as well. Jefferson quickly accepted. The Louisiana Purchase doubled the territory of the United States and eventually formed all or part of 13 new states.

★ TASK

You and several friends work for a manufacturer of educational toys and games. The company plans to market a series of jigsaw puzzle maps highlighting the growth of the United States. Your task is to create the model for the puzzle showing the political face of North America immediately following the Louisiana Purchase.

★ AUDIENCE

Your audience is students and adults who are potential customers for the puzzle.

★ PURPOSE

The purpose of your project is to help your audience understand the political divisions that existed in 1803. Include the names, relative sizes, and locations of existing states, United States territories, and territories still owned by European nations.

★ PROCEDURE

1. Consult the Performance Task Assessment Lists for a Model, a Map, and a Cooperative Group Management Plan to assist you in planning, designing, and constructing your project.
2. Agree on research, design, and construction tasks for each group member.
3. With your assigned teammates, research to discover the exact and relative locations of the states and territories that apply.
4. Together plan a map that accurately shows the necessary information.
5. Cooperate with your teammates to create a prototype (rough model) of the puzzle map. Share your prototype with another group to obtain feedback.
6. As a team make revisions, as appropriate.
7. Create your final jigsaw puzzle map.

★ ASSESSMENT

1. Use the performance task assessment lists suggested to evaluate the various parts of your project.
2. Add or improve elements at each stage as needed.
3. Complete a final self-assessment before sharing your model with the class.

Name ______________________ Date ______________ Class __________

★ Performance Assessment Activity 10

Use with Chapter 10

The Latin American Liberators

BACKGROUND

In the early 1800s the people of Latin America also sought self-rule. Tired of Spanish exploitation, they rebelled. Revolutionary leaders came forward. Some earned the same respect among their people as George Washington and Thomas Jefferson achieved in the United States. They became legends who inspired future generations.

TASK

You are a sculptor. A Latin American country has commissioned you to design a monument to one of its liberators. This memorial statue will stand outside the country's embassy in Washington, D.C. Your task is to create a clay model of this figure and write an inscription that will appear on the statue's base.

AUDIENCE

Your audience is visitors from this country and abroad who will view the statue and react to the message you wish to communicate.

PURPOSE

The purpose of your project is to help your audience understand this individual's contribution to the spread of democracy in the Americas.

PROCEDURE

1. Consult the Performance Task Assessment Lists for a Model and an Individual Performance Task Management Plan to assist you in planning, designing, and making your sculpture.
2. Research and select a Latin American revolutionary leader.
3. Conduct further research to learn as much as possible about your chosen leader.
4. Create prototypes (rough models) of your subject and write a first draft of the inscription that will appear on the statue's base.
5. Share your examples with a partner to obtain feedback and to help you select your best creations. Make revisions if necessary.
6. Prepare your final presentation.

ASSESSMENT

1. Use the Performance Task Assessment Lists for a Model and an Individual Performance Task Management Plan to evaluate each stage of your project.
2. Add or improve elements at each stage as needed.
3. Complete a final self-assessment of your work before displaying your model.

Name ______________________ Date ______________ Class ________

★ **Performance Assessment Activity 11**

Use with Chapter 11

History as Drama

BACKGROUND

People make history. Their struggles and dreams, their triumphs and tragedies form the backdrop for every great battle, sweeping social change, and difficult migration. This is why history makes great drama. It is the story of people.

TASK

You and your friends are members of a theater company, specializing in historical drama. A television network plans to produce a series dramatizing events from United States history. You have agreed to write and perform a pilot episode highlighting an incident in the Age of Jackson.

AUDIENCE

Your teacher, other students, and interested adults are your audience.

PURPOSE

The purpose of your pilot episode is to entertain and inform. It should help your audience comprehend how and why one major historical event unfolded and to understand the views of the people involved.

PROCEDURE

1. Consult the Performance Task Assessment Lists for a Cooperative Group Management Plan and a Role Play to guide you in planning.
2. Form a team with at least three other students. Together decide on an event from the Jackson era that had an impact on people for years to come, such as the Bank War, states' rights challenges, the Trail of Tears, the Second Seminole War, or the Panic of 1837.
3. Conduct research to learn as much as possible about your chosen topic.
4. Share what you discover with your teammates and decide what information to include in your production.
5. Together decide on the characters (including a narrator), and assign each group member a role. Characters can write their dialogue as you work through the plot together.
6. With your team, create scenery and stage props.
7. Rehearse your episode and revise the dialogue for all characters as needed.
8. Present your episode.

ASSESSMENT

1. Refer to the performance task assessment lists suggested to review your work on this project.
2. Add or improve elements at each stage as needed.
3. Complete a final self-assessment of your project.

Name ______________________ Date ______________ Class ________

★ Performance Assessment Activity 12

Use with Chapter 12

Across the Wide Prairie

BACKGROUND

In the mid-1800s the United States again dramatically increased its territory. Texas entered the Union in 1845. In 1848 Great Britain recognized the United States's claims to the Oregon Territory and yielded land that became Oregon, Washington, Idaho, and parts of two other states. In 1848 Mexico surrendered California and territory that eventually formed all or part of six additional states. Settlers soon began streaming into these newly acquired lands.

TASK

You are a graphic artist. A wagon master in St. Louis wants to advertise his services. He leads wagon trains full of settlers across the prairie to the Oregon Territory. He has commissioned you to create a poster.

AUDIENCE

Your audience is single adults and families living along the East Coast who are interested in moving to the Western frontier. Students, teachers, and other invited guests should play these adults and families.

PURPOSE

The purpose of your poster is to persuade your audience to join with others and form a wagon train traveling to the Oregon Territory.

PROCEDURE

1. Consult the Performance Task Assessment List for a Poster to guide you from initial planning to final display.
2. Research to discover more about wagon trains and features of the Oregon Territory that appealed to early settlers.
3. Choose images to illustrate your message.
4. Draft an attention-getting slogan to accompany your artwork.
5. Design your poster.
6. Share your work with a partner to get feedback and suggestions for improvement; revise as needed.
7. Create your final poster.

ASSESSMENT

1. Use the Performance Task Assessment List for a Poster when reviewing your work.
2. Add or improve elements at each stage as needed.
3. Complete a final self-assessment of your poster before displaying it.

Name ______________________ Date ______________ Class ________

★ Performance Assessment Activity 13

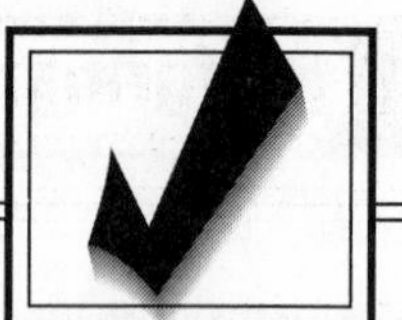

Use with Chapter 13

Contrasting Lifestyles

BACKGROUND

In the late 1700s people from the Northern and Southern states worked together to form a nation. By the mid-1800s economic and social forces threatened the Union. The North had a strong industrial base. The South was agricultural. Economic differences caused disagreements and resentment. Abolitionist sentiment grew in Northern states which had outlawed enslavement. Southern states defended slavery. The two regions drifted apart.

TASK

You and several friends teach American history. You are planning how to show life in the United States between 1820 and 1860. You decide to create a bulletin board comparing life in the North and life in the South during these years.

AUDIENCE

Students, other teachers, and instructional supervisors are your audience.

PURPOSE

The purpose of your bulletin board is to help your audience visualize the differences that existed between the regions of the country in the mid-1800s.

PROCEDURE

1. Consult the Performance Task Assessment Lists for a Bulletin Board Display, a Map, and a Cooperative Group Management Plan as guides to completing your tasks.
2. With your teammates research to discover as much as possible about the different social and economic conditions in the North and the South between 1820 and 1860.
3. Agree upon research, design, and construction tasks for each group member.
4. Complete your research. Share information with your teammates.
5. As a team sketch ideas for the map and other elements for your bulletin board. Decide how you will organize these materials. You might include magazine or newspaper pictures, photographs, or original drawings.
6. Share your ideas with another group, obtain suggestions, and revise.
7. Together create your final bulletin board display.

ASSESSMENT

1. Use the performance task assessment lists suggested to evaluate your bulletin board plan.
2. Check to see that you have included all elements.
3. Organize all the materials that you plan to put on your bulletin board.
4. Complete a final self-assessment before you share your project.

Name ______________________ Date ______________ Class __________

★ Performance Assessment Activity 14

Use with Chapter 14

Liberty and Justice for All

BACKGROUND

A social revolution swept the United States between 1820 and 1860. Most states passed laws guaranteeing children a free public education (through the eighth grade). Many reformers demanded equal rights and expanded opportunities for women. Others urged better treatment of prisoners and the mentally disabled. Abolitionists fought for racial equality and an end to enslavement.

TASK

You are an advocate, or supporter, for social reform. A civic group has asked you to address an educational workshop it is sponsoring about the reform movement. The movement has inspired you to take action and qualifies you to answer the audience's questions.

AUDIENCE

Your audience is students, teachers, and other invited guests.

PURPOSE

The purpose of your presentation is to educate your audience about the history, achievements, and current goals of your reform movement.

PROCEDURE

1. Consult the Performance Task Assessment Lists for a Research Report and an Oral Presentation as guides to completing your tasks.
2. Select one of the reforms discussed in your text. Research to discover as much information as possible about the history of this movement, its founders and champions, and current unresolved issues.
3. Using the information you have discovered, prepare note cards with specific details that you will include in your presentation.
4. Design and create visual aids that will highlight key points in your presentation.
5. Practice your presentation and share your visual aids with a classmate for feedback and suggestions for improvement, then revise.
6. Give a formal presentation of your work to your audience.

ASSESSMENT

1. Use the Performance Task Assessment Lists for a Research Report and an Oral Presentation to check your work and add to or improve it as needed.
2. Think about what you might do to improve your oral delivery if you need to make a speech in the future.
3. Complete a final self-assessment of your entire project.

Name ______________________ Date ______________ Class __________

★ Performance Assessment Activity 15

Use with Chapter 15

Interpreting the Compromise Vote

BACKGROUND

Most Southerners opposed the Republican platform in 1860. Some historians believe the majority of Southerners also opposed secession. As evidence they point to the popular vote in 1860. Stephen A. Douglas, a Northerner, and John Bell, a Southerner, were compromise candidates, or candidates who favored agreements between the North and the South rather than conflict about states' rights and slavery. In 14 slave states Douglas and Bell, combined, received 124,000 more votes than John C. Breckinridge, the candidate of the secessionists. Interestingly, the combined votes for the two compromise candidates nationwide also exceeded Abraham Lincoln's total vote.

TASK

You are a statistician. A historian, publishing a book about secession, has asked you to create a graph of the 1860 presidential election. Your graph will illustrate the outcome of a nationwide three-way race if votes for Douglas and Bell are combined.

AUDIENCE

Your audience is students, teachers, and other potential readers of the book.

PURPOSE

The purpose of your graph is to help your audience understand the strong support among voters in 1860 for compromise on secession issues.

PROCEDURE

1. Consult the Performance Task Assessment List for a Graph as a guide to help you in the completion of this project.
2. Refer to information provided in your text and conduct further research to discover as much as possible about the results of the 1860 election.
3. Design a graph that shows the popular vote in numbers and the percentages that would have been received by the candidates if the ballots for Douglas and Bell were combined. You might use a bar graph, circle graph, or pictograph, or a graph that uses pictures as symbols to represent quantities.
4. Share your work with a friend to make certain it is accurate and complete. Revise your graph if necessary.
5. Create your final graph.

ASSESSMENT

1. Use the Performance Task Assessment List for a Graph to check your work.
2. Add or improve elements at each stage as needed.

Name ______________________ Date ______________ Class ________

★ Performance Assessment Activity 16

Use with Chapter 16

Profiles of Military Leaders

★ BACKGROUND

The Civil War fascinates many Americans. Each year thousands of tourists visit Civil War battle sites. Many people collect memorabilia from the period, including uniforms, flags, diaries, and photographs. Others belong to book clubs or subscribe to magazines specializing in the subject. Public television broadcast a 10-hour documentary titled *The Civil War*. This work attracted one of the largest viewing audiences in public television history.

★ TASK

You are a freelance writer. You regularly contribute articles to a magazine devoted to the American Civil War. The publisher has asked you to write the first in a series of biographical profiles about Northern and Southern Civil War generals.

★ AUDIENCE

Students, teachers, and interested adults who might subscribe to the magazine make up your audience.

★ PURPOSE

Your biographical sketch examines the background, achievements, and historical assessment of one Civil War military general.

★ PROCEDURE

1. Consult the Performance Task Assessment Lists for a Research Report and a Newspaper Article.
2. Select one Civil War general who interests you.
3. Refer to the text and conduct further research to discover as much as possible about your subject.
4. Write a first draft of your article. Create an attention-getting title.
5. Share your draft with a friend to obtain feedback and suggestions. Revise by adding accurate, vivid supporting details. Check for accuracy.
6. Write the final draft of your biographical profile.

★ ASSESSMENT

1. Use the performance task assessment lists suggested to evaluate your magazine article.
2. Complete a final self-assessment of your work before sharing it.
3. Combine your article with others in your class to create a biographical portfolio of Civil War generals.

Name ______________________ Date ______________ Class __________

★ Performance Assessment Activity 17

Use with Chapter 17

You Can Make a Difference!

BACKGROUND

In March 1865 President Abraham Lincoln signed a bill creating the Freedmen's Bureau. This organization characterized Lincoln's vision of Reconstruction. The Freedmen's Bureau provided food, clothing, and medical care for formerly enslaved African Americans and white Southerners in need. The Bureau workers also founded schools for African Americans. Many individuals taught in these schools on a volunteer basis.

TASK

You are a volunteer teacher for the Freedmen's Bureau. You have returned home for a visit. A local civic group has asked you to give an oral presentation explaining to others the importance of the work you do.

AUDIENCE

Your audience is students, teachers, and other adults who have come to hear your presentation.

PURPOSE

Your purpose is to inform your audience about the educational mission of the Freedmen's Bureau and to persuade others to volunteer their services.

PROCEDURE

1. Consult the Performance Task Assessment Lists for a Research Report and an Oral Presentation as guides to completing your task.
2. Refer to your text and conduct further research to discover as much information as possible about the Freedmen's Bureau.
3. Using the information you have discovered, prepare note cards with specific details you will include in your oral presentation.
4. Design and create visual aids that will highlight your main points.
5. Practice your presentation and share your visual aids with a classmate for feedback and suggestions for improvement; then revise.
6. Give a formal presentation of your work to your audience.

ASSESSMENT

1. Use the performance task assessment lists suggested to check your work and add to or improve it as needed.
2. Think about what you might do to improve your organization or delivery if you make a speech in the future.
3. Complete a final self-assessment of your entire project.

Name ______________________ Date ______________ Class ________

★ **Performance Assessment Activity 18**

Use with Chapter 18

Coming to America

BACKGROUND

Millions of people immigrated to the United States between 1870 and 1900. They came from all parts of the world. Many came in search of good jobs. Others sought to escape oppression. All of them shared a dream. In America they would find a land of opportunity. They would earn the rewards of hard work. They would have their rights as individuals respected.

TASK

You are a songwriter. A producer is making a movie about immigrants coming to the United States in the late 1800s. The producer has asked you to write a theme song. The film audience will hear this song as the immigrants see the American shoreline for the first time.

AUDIENCE

Your audience is made up of children, teenagers, and adults who watch the movie.

PURPOSE

Your purpose is to write a song that captures the mood and the thoughts of immigrants who have come to the United States seeking freedom and opportunity.

PROCEDURE

1. Consult the Performance Task Assessment List for an Original Song to assist you in writing your movie theme.
2. Refer to your text and conduct research to discover more about the reasons people gave for immigrating to the United States in the late 1800s.
3. Locate and listen to examples of patriotic songs about the United States.
4. Write lyrics for your song, consulting a rhyming dictionary if necessary.
   a. Use words and phrases from your research.
   b. Create a lively phrase that can be repeated as a chorus.
5. Exchange your work with a partner for review; revise and prepare a final copy of your song.
6. Perform your song for your classmates and teacher. Include an instrumental accompaniment if you wish.

ASSESSMENT

1. Use the Performance Task Assessment List for an Original Song to check your work.
2. Add or improve elements at each stage as needed.
3. Complete a final self-assessment of your song.

Name ______________________ Date ______________ Class ________

★ **Performance Assessment Activity 19**

Use with Chapter 19

How the Web Changed the World

BACKGROUND

In the early part of the 1990s, people who wanted to communicate made phone calls and sent letters. They found information at the library or in current magazines and newspapers. Most did not have friendships with people in other countries. Electronic communication technology changed all that. By the mid-1990s, business cards, personal stationery, and magazine mastheads contained e-mail addresses. Students in universities and some public schools did research on the Internet and "talked" with others all over the world via the World Wide Web.

TASK

The editor of a magazine that focuses on future trends has asked you to write an article that predicts how new communications technologies will change the future. The article will identify broad areas such as education, politics, and business and explore ways that electronic communications technologies will affect these institutions.

AUDIENCE

Your audience will be the readers of the magazine, both adults and young people.

PURPOSE

Your article will identify areas of change and help inform the readers about how to prepare for the future.

PROCEDURE

1. Consult the Performance Task Assessment List for a Research Report.
2. Decide which areas will be the focus of your article.
3. Complete your research. With the help of the research materials, decide how you think several basic areas will change because of electronic communications technologies.
4. Decide on a plan for how you will present your ideas most effectively.
5. Write a draft of your magazine article and share it with a classmate for suggestions.
6. Make revisions to your draft and prepare your final article.

ASSESSMENT

1. Use the Performance Task Assessment List for a Research Report to evaluate your project.
2. Discuss what you might do differently if you do a similar project in the future.

Name ______________________ Date ______________ Class __________

★ Scoring Rubric

Use with Activities 8, 13

A Bulletin Board Display

S The bulletin board is outstanding. It is so attractive, creative, interesting, and compelling that the audience will enjoy viewing it again and again. The ideas are presented clearly. The artistic and technical aspects of the project are eloquent.

T The bulletin board immediately catches your eye through the use of humor, design, or other similar strategies. The message is clear and the concepts are appropriately and accurately presented. The design is simple, organized, and effective. The bulletin board seems neither too full nor too scanty. The illustrations, statements, and other design elements combine neatly and effectively.

U The bulletin board is similar to the one receiving a rating of **T**, except there are one or two important elements that are not excellent.

V The bulletin board is similar to the one receiving a rating of **W**, except there are one or two important elements that are well done.

W The bulletin board display is not interesting or appealing. Important concepts are unclear. Information is missing or incorrect. The design is cluttered or unorganized. The mix of illustrations, statements, and other design elements does not accomplish the intended purpose. The project is messy.

X The bulletin board is very poorly done.

Name ______________________ Date ______________ Class __________

★ **Performance Task Assessment List**

Use with Activities 8, 13

A Bulletin Board Display

ELEMENT ASSESSMENT	POINTS POSSIBLE	EARNED ASSESSMENT SELF	TEACHER
1. The bulletin board is attractive, creative, and interesting.			
2. The ideas are presented clearly.			
3. The bulletin board uses humor, interesting design, or other features.			
4. The bulletin board's message is clear.			
5. Information is appropriate and accurate.			
6. The bulletin board does not appear too full or empty.			
7. The illustrations, statements, and other design elements work well together.			
8. The overall appearance is neat and presentable.			
Total			

Name ______________________ Date ______________ Class __________

★ Scoring Rubric

Use with Activity 15

A Graph

S The graph is outstanding in its ability to clearly and easily convey accurate information. The project is visually pleasing and interesting. The key is concise and accurate.

T The student has organized the information with a reasonable amount of accuracy. Symbols and color coding are clear and accurate. The graph is easy to read and interpret; the key is accurate. The graph provides important information.

U The graph is similar to the one receiving a rating of **T**, except there are one or two important elements that are not excellent.

V The graph is similar to the one receiving a rating of **W**, except there are one or two important elements that are well done.

W The information provided in this project is not accurate or is not central to the concept being explored. Symbols and color coding are confusing or inaccurate. The work is unappealing and difficult to read. The key is misleading or unclear.

X The graph is very poorly done.

Name ____________________ Date ____________ Class ________

★ Performance Task Assessment List

Use with Activity 15

A Graph

ELEMENT ASSESSMENT	POINTS POSSIBLE	EARNED ASSESSMENT SELF	EARNED ASSESSMENT TEACHER
1. The project is attractive and interesting.	______	______	______
2. The key is clear and accurate.	______	______	______
3. Information is well organized and accurate.	______	______	______
4. Symbols and color coding are clear and accurate.	______	______	______
5. The graph is easy to read and interpret.	______	______	______
6. The graph provides important information about the main idea(s).	______	______	______
Total	______	______	______

Name ______________________ Date ______________ Class ___________

★ Scoring Rubric

Use with Activities 2, 9, 13

A Map

S The student's map is outstanding, clearly and easily conveying accurate information. It is visually pleasing and interesting. The key is concise and accurate.

T The student has organized information and encoded it into the map with a reasonable amount of accuracy. Distinct areas are outlined and identified effectively. Symbols and color coding for data are clear and accurately applied. The map is easy to read and interpret. The key is accurate.

U The map is like one receiving a rating of **T**, except there are one or two important elements that are not excellent.

V The map is like one receiving a rating of **W**, except there are one or two important elements that are well done.

W The data used for the map is not clearly organized. Symbols and color coding are confusing and inaccurate. The map is unappealing and difficult to read. The key is garbled and misleading.

X The map is very poorly done.

Name ______________________ Date ______________ Class ________

★ Performance Task Assessment List

Use with Activities 2, 9, 13

A Map

ELEMENT ASSESSMENT	POINTS POSSIBLE	EARNED ASSESSMENT SELF	EARNED ASSESSMENT TEACHER
1. The information is well organized.	________	________	________
2. Separate areas are outlined and identified clearly and accurately.	________	________	________
3. Symbols and color coding are clear and effective.	________	________	________
4. The map includes a key in which all symbols are accurately identified.	________	________	________
5. The map is neatly drawn and is easy to read and interpret.	________	________	________
Total	________	________	________

Name ______________________ Date ______________ Class __________

★ Scoring Rubric

Use with Activities 1, 9, 10

A Model

S The model cleverly and clearly demonstrates an important concept. Technical quality is high with every component accurately drawn to scale. The model simulates the elements of the real item and is of high artistic quality.

T The student has drawn a plan for the model that identifies all its parts and dimensions. The plan includes clear, written explanations of how the model resembles the real item and how the model is different. The model simulates the important elements of the real item in the ways intended. Colors, labels, and other strategies help clarify what the model was designed to demonstrate. The model is sturdy, safe to use, neat, and presentable.

U The model is similar to the one receiving a rating of **T**, except there are one or two important elements that are poor or technically incorrect.

V The model is similar to the one receiving a rating of **W**, except there are one or two important elements that are well done.

W The plan for the model is incomplete, inaccurate, or does not clearly show the parts and dimensions. The explanations of how the model is similar to and dissimilar from the real item are incomplete or inaccurate. The constructed model does not work well, or it completely fails to work. Needed colors, labels, and other such aids are missing or inadequate. The model is not safe. It is not neat and presentable.

X The plan for the model is very poorly done, and the constructed model is very inaccurate.

Name ______________________ Date ______________ Class __________

★ Performance Task Assessment List

Use with Activities 1, 9, 10

A Model

ELEMENT ASSESSMENT	POINTS POSSIBLE	EARNED ASSESSMENT SELF	TEACHER
1. A clear plan of the model is drawn to scale.	______	______	______
2. The plan shows the model's parts and measurements.	______	______	______
3. The plan includes explanations of how the model represents the real item and how it is different.	______	______	______
4. The model shows the important elements of the real item.	______	______	______
5. Colors, labels, and other such clues help make clear what the model shows.	______	______	______
6. The model is sturdy and safe to use.	______	______	______
7. The model is neat and presentable.	______	______	______
Total	______	______	______

Name ______________________ Date ______________ Class __________

★ Scoring Rubric

Use with Activities 5, 16

A Newspaper Article

S The quality of the article is exceptional. It conveys the story in a smooth and engaging style. It holds the readers' interest. Appropriate quotes and details are woven into the article. Photographs are highly informative. The headline is memorable.

T The article is interesting and concise. The theme is immediately apparent, and the article develops smoothly. Appropriate details support the theme, and quotes are used correctly. The vocabulary is appropriate to the audience. The article is ethical and factually correct. Any humor used is in good taste. The headline is effective. Photographs are clear, interesting, and show active rather than passive poses. Photograph captions are in the correct format.

U The article is like one receiving a rating of **T**, except there are one or two important elements that are not excellent.

V The article is like one receiving a rating of **W**, except there are one or two important elements that are of good quality.

W The article reads like minutes to a meeting. The theme is unclear, and the writing disorganized. Details are missing or inappropriate. Quotations are overused or incorrect. Elements of the article are in poor taste. The headline is dull. Photographs are of poor quality or lack interest. Captions are incomplete, or the format is incorrect.

X The article is very poor and unacceptable.

Name ________________ Date ________________ Class ________

★ **Performance Task Assessment List**

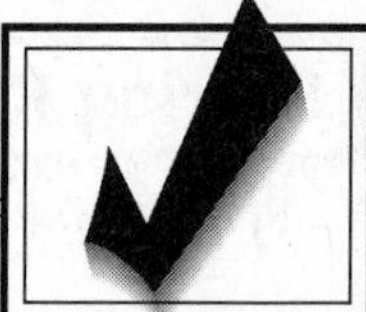

Use with Activities 5, 16

A Newspaper Article

ELEMENT ASSESSMENT	POINTS POSSIBLE	EARNED ASSESSMENT SELF	EARNED ASSESSMENT TEACHER
1. The facts are correct.			
2. Quotations are recorded exactly word for word.			
3. Quotations are used appropriately.			
4. The writing flows smoothly.			
5. The main idea of the article is clear.			
6. The readers found the article interesting.			
7. The writing is concise, clear, and complete.			
8. There are sufficient supporting details.			
9. The style and vocabulary are appropriate.			
10. Humor is used in good taste.			
11. It is free of errors in spelling or grammar.			
12. The headline is both "attention-grabbing" and appropriate to the story.			
13. Photographs clearly illustrate the meaning of the story.			
14. Photographs are interesting and appropriately captioned.			
Total			

Name ______________________ Date ______________ Class __________

★ Scoring Rubric

Use with Activities 7, 14, 17

An Oral Presentation

S The presentation is exciting and expressive. The speaker shows a flair for communicating with the audience. Humor and creativity are clearly present. The speaker is confident and at ease.

T The presenter speaks in a clear voice and at an appropriate rate. The speaker is interesting, enthusiastic, and makes eye contact with the entire audience. The speaker's dress and posture are appropriate. The presentation is well organized with a beginning, a body of information, and a conclusion. A strong central theme is supported by main ideas. There are clear transitions. Details and examples clarify the main ideas. The student clearly understands the core curriculum. Visual aids are well done and make the presentation more interesting and meaningful. The speaker allows time for the audience to think and involves the audience in some active way.

U The presentation is similar to one receiving a rating of **T**, except there are one or two elements that are less polished.

V The presentation is similar to one receiving a rating of **W**, except there are one or two elements that are relatively well done.

W The presenter is difficult to hear or speaks at an incorrect rate of speed. The speaker lacks interest or enthusiasm, appearing to read the presentation. Eye contact is poor or spotty. The speaker is not well groomed. The presentation lacks organization. Details or examples are insufficient or inappropriate. Some information may be incomplete or inaccurate. It is not clear that the student understands the core curriculum. Visual aids are poorly done or do not enhance the information discussed. The speaker does not actively involve the audience.

X The presentation is very poorly organized and delivered.

Name ________________ Date ____________ Class ________

★ **Performance Task Assessment List**

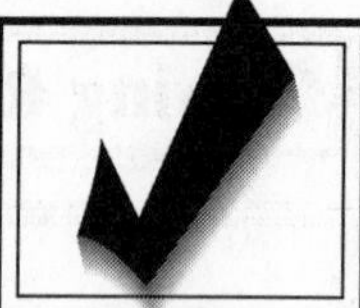

Use with Activities 7, 14, 17

An Oral Presentation

ELEMENT ASSESSMENT	POINTS POSSIBLE	EARNED ASSESSMENT SELF	EARNED ASSESSMENT TEACHER
1. Everyone can hear the speaker clearly.			
2. The speaker is enthusiastic.			
3. The presentation's pace is even.			
4. The speaker makes eye contact with individuals throughout the audience.			
5. The speaker is dressed appropriately, is well groomed, and has excellent posture.			
6. The presentation is organized with a beginning, middle, and conclusion.			
7. The main ideas support the theme.			
8. There are enough details to support the main ideas.			
9. The speaker knows the subject.			
10. Visual aids are well done.			
11. The speaker involves the audience.			
12. The length is appropriate.			
13. The presentation communicates effectively.			
Total			

Name ______________________ Date ______________ Class ____________

★ Scoring Rubric

Use with Activities 6, 18

An Original Song

S The song is outstanding. The music or rhythm is masterfully adapted or composed. The lyrics are memorable. The entire composition is extremely appropriate for the intended audience.

T The student composed the original song using a recognized musical form. Rhythm or rhyme scheme is used throughout the lyrics of the song. The pitch is appropriate for the singer. The lyrics flow to the pitch variations or rhythm of the music. The lyrics convey the intended message. The lyrics and rhythm or music work together to achieve the desired effect on the target audience.

U This song is generally as good as one receiving a rating of **T**, but it is uneven with some less-developed areas.

V This song is similar to that receiving a rating of **W**, but it has one or two areas that are better developed.

W The song is not very original. The student does not adapt the work to a recognized musical structure. The pitch range is not well matched to the voice. A rhythmic beat is absent or unreliable. The words do not convey the intended message and are not memorable. The words and music or rhythm do not work well together.

X The song is very poorly composed.

Name ______________________ Date ______________ Class __________

★ **Performance Task Assessment List**

Use with Activities 6, 18

An Original Song

ELEMENT ASSESSMENT	POINTS POSSIBLE	EARNED ASSESSMENT SELF	TEACHER
1. Rhythm or rhyme is clear.	________	________	________
2. The pitch is appropriate for the singer and instrument.	________	________	________
3. Special use of words or tunes adds interest to the piece.	________	________	________
4. The words convey the message to the the audience.	________	________	________
Total	________	________	________

Name ______________________ Date ______________ Class __________

★ Scoring Rubric

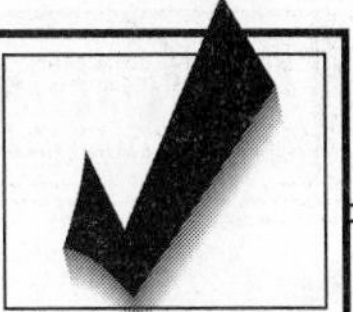

Use with Activities 3, 12

A Poster

S The poster is outstanding, creative, and communicates clearly.

T The theme of the poster is clear immediately. As you study it, more and more information is evident. The main or general ideas are supported by appropriate, specific details. Main ideas expand the theme. Information is accurate. The student comprehends the core curriculum. Space, shapes, textures, and colors provide information and make the poster easier to understand. Pictures, photographs, drawings, diagrams, graphs, and other elements add clarity. The words are appropriate for the topic and audience. The form of the poster reflects the author's purpose. The overall impression is of one complete work and not just a collection of pieces. The work is very neat.

U The poster resembles one receiving a rating of **T**, except one or two important elements are not excellent.

V The poster resembles one receiving a rating of **W**, except one or two important elements are well done.

W The poster is difficult to understand even when it is explained. The work lacks clear main ideas. Some information is incomplete or inaccurate. The student does not show a mastery of the core curriculum. Spaces, shapes, textures, and colors are missing or ineffectual. Pictures, photographs, drawings, diagrams, graphs and other elements are missing or inappropriate. The work is sloppy.

X The poster is very poorly done.

Name ______________________ Date ______________ Class __________

★ Performance Task Assessment List

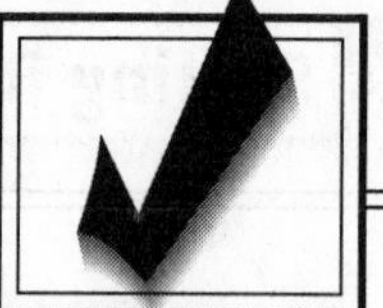

Use with Activities 3, 12

A Poster

ELEMENT ASSESSMENT	POINTS POSSIBLE	EARNED ASSESSMENT SELF	TEACHER
1. The main theme of the poster is clear. The title helps explain this theme.	______	______	______
2. Appropriate details support main ideas.	______	______	______
3. The ideas are connected to the main theme.	______	______	______
4. Information is complete and accurate.	______	______	______
5. Space, shapes, textures, and colors provide information and make the poster easier to understand.	______	______	______
6. Pictures, photographs, drawings, diagrams, graphs, and other elements add information and make ideas clear.	______	______	______
7. The words are appropriate for the topic and audience.	______	______	______
8. The work is very neat and presentable.	______	______	______
Total	______	______	______

Name ______________________ Date ______________ Class ________

★ Scoring Rubric

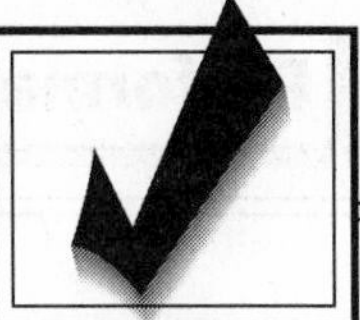

Use with Activities 4, 5, 7, 14, 16, 17, 19

A Research Report

S This research report is exceptional in all elements. It is expressive, informative, and achieves its purpose with the intended audience.

T This paper is uniformly well organized, logically developed, and engaging. A thesis statement clearly defines the topic and presents the main argument. The introduction describes what the author proposes to say or prove, provides a context for the topic, and lays out a style and organizational plan. Each paragraph has a clear topic sentence and appropriate supporting details that work together to develop the thesis. All facts are correct. The conclusion effectively demonstrates that the author proved what was stated in the thesis. The paper is concise with excellent grammar and mechanics throughout. The author's mastery of the concepts is evident. All resource materials are properly referenced. The paper is neat and presentable.

U This paper is almost as good as that receiving a rating of **T**, but it is uneven with some less-developed elements.

V The paper is similar to that receiving a rating of **W**, but it has one or two important elements that are better developed.

W The paper is unorganized and poorly developed. The thesis statement is unclear. The introduction fails to explain the purpose of the paper, context for the thesis, or provide an organization plan for the report. Some paragraphs do not have main ideas or supporting details. Some information is inaccurate, the arguments unconvincing. Errors in grammar or mechanics are present. Sources of information are not cited. The paper is messy.

X The research report is extremely weak in all areas.

Name ______________________ Date ______________ Class ________

★ **Performance Task Assessment List**

Use with Activities 4, 5, 7, 14, 16, 17, 19

A Research Report

ELEMENT ASSESSMENT	POINTS POSSIBLE	EARNED ASSESSMENT SELF	TEACHER
1. The topic is clear and the introduction effective.	______	______	______
2. The body of the paper is organized into paragraphs with clear main ideas and appropriate supporting details.	______	______	______
3. The conclusion shows that the author has kept the paper's purpose in mind.	______	______	______
4. The author clearly demonstrates essential knowledge of the topic.	______	______	______
5. The author's own thinking is the focus of this report.	______	______	______
6. The author accurately and completely references all sources of information.	______	______	______
7. Visual aids, such as graphs and diagrams, if used, help explain the information.	______	______	______
8. Spelling and grammar are correct.	______	______	______
9. The report is neat and presentable.	______	______	______
Total	______	______	______

Name ______________________ Date ______________ Class __________

★ Scoring Rubric

Use with Activity 11

A Role Play

S The role play is exceptional. The story line and characters use creativity or humor to send a clear message to the intended audience.

T Overall, the role play is excellent and communicates its message to the audience. The actors or actresses can be seen and heard. The information and dialogue are appropriate to the topic and audience. The characters are well suited to the topic and are well developed by the cast. The props add to the effectiveness of the role play. The role play is well organized, focuses on the topic, and is of appropriate length.

U The work is generally as good as one receiving a rating of **T**, but it is uneven with some less-developed areas.

V This work is similar to that receiving a rating of **W**, but it has one or two areas that are better developed.

W The role play does not communicate the proposed message to the intended audience. The actors or actresses cannot be seen or heard. All characters may not be suited to the topic or developed by the cast. The props are lacking or are distracting. The role play is disorganized or unfocused or is too short or too long. Verbal or nonverbal information presented in the role play is not accurate.

X The role play is very poor in all respects.

Name ______________________ Date ______________ Class __________

★ Performance Task Assessment List

Use with Activity 11

A Role Play

ELEMENT ASSESSMENT	POINTS POSSIBLE	EARNED ASSESSMENT SELF	TEACHER
1. The entire audience can hear the speakers.	______	______	______
2. The dialogue is appropriate to both the topic and the audience.	______	______	______
3. The characters are suitable for the topic of the role play.	______	______	______
4. The actors develop the characters well.	______	______	______
5. The props used in the role play add to the interest and message.	______	______	______
6. Everyone can see the actions.	______	______	______
7. The role play is organized and focused.	______	______	______
8. The information in the role play, both spoken and nonverbal, is accurate and appropriate.	______	______	______
9. The role play is the appropriate length.	______	______	______
Total	______	______	______

Name ______________________ Date ______________ Class __________

★ Scoring Rubric

Use with Activities 1, 4, 9, 11, 13

A Cooperative Group Management Plan

S The plan is exceptional and could serve as an example of excellent work. The group members have simulated, to an extraordinary degree, how teamwork is used in the larger world to achieve a common goal.

T The plan is excellent. It encourages full, enthusiastic participation and diverse ideas. The purpose statement and audience description reflect a thorough understanding of the goal. Care and foresight in planning encourages equal task distribution and individual responsibility. It sets realistic time frames for completion of individual tasks and requires minimal adjustment. The presentation assures the fullest possible participation and gives full credit for contributions.

U The work is generally as good as one receiving a rating of **T**, but it is uneven with some less-developed areas.

V The work is similar to that receiving a rating of **W**, but it has one or two areas that are better developed.

W The plan does not accomplish its purpose. Full participation is not evident, and a diversity of ideas does not emerge. The purpose statement is vague, and the audience description inadequate. Tasks are not equitable. Problems are unforeseen. Individual accountability is not clear, and the time frames are unrealistic. Unnecessary redistribution of tasks and adjustment of time frames disrupt the process. The plan does not allow for full participation or appropriate credit. The work is sloppy.

X The plan is very poorly done in all respects.

Name ______________________ Date ______________ Class __________

★ Performance Task Assessment List

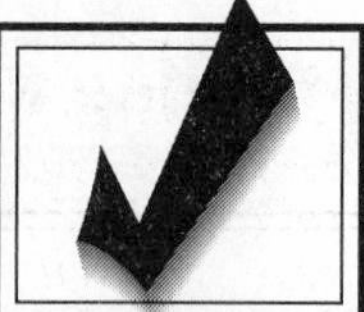

Use with Activities 1, 4, 9, 11, 13

A Cooperative Group Management Plan

ELEMENT ASSESSMENT	POINTS POSSIBLE	EARNED ASSESSMENT SELF	EARNED ASSESSMENT TEACHER
1. Team members agree on a purpose statement and an audience description.	______	______	______
2. Team members agree on a list of tasks required to achieve the goal.	______	______	______
3. Team members agree on scheduled dates for checking progress toward the goal.	______	______	______
4. Problems that might interfere with completion are identified and solved.	______	______	______
5. Tasks are divided fairly.	______	______	______
6. Each member has approved the plan by initialing beside his or her name on a printed list of group members.	______	______	______
PROCESS			
7. Team members adjust individual tasks to divide labor fairly.	______	______	______
PRODUCT			
8. Team members agree on a format for the presentation of the product. **a.** Each member plays an active role.	______	______	______
b. Each member receives full credit.	______	______	______
FINAL ANALYSIS			
9. Each member has signed the final plan to indicate his or her approval of participation in the process and presentation.	______	______	______
10. The management plan is neat.	______	______	______
Total	______	______	______

Name ______________________ Date ______________ Class ____________

★ Scoring Rubric

Use with Activities 8, 10

An Individual Performance Task Management Plan

S The plan is a model of excellence. It states its purpose and audience description briefly. Task identification is masterful, and the logical progression perfect. Solutions to overcome problems are clever. The internal time frames for checking progress reflect a thorough understanding of what is required to complete each task.

T The plan is excellent, with a precise purpose statement and descriptions of the audience. Tasks are accurately identified. Organization is logical, and solutions to problems are reasonable. Deadlines are realistic for completion of each task.

U The work is generally as good as one receiving a rating of **T**, but it is uneven, with some less-developed areas.

V The work is similar to that receiving a rating of **W**, but it has one or two areas that are better developed.

W The plan is poorly done. The purpose is unclear. The target audience is not well defined. The list of tasks is incomplete or unorganized. Problems are unrecognized or have impractical solutions. The deadlines are unrealistic, and show that the student lacks a grasp of what must be accomplished for the completion of each task.

X The plan is very poorly done in all respects.

Name ______________________ Date ______________ Class __________

★ Performance Task Assessment List

Use with Activities 8, 10

An Individual Performance Task Management Plan

ELEMENT ASSESSMENT	POINTS POSSIBLE	EARNED ASSESSMENT SELF	EARNED ASSESSMENT TEACHER
1. The plan states the student's name and due date for completion.	______	______	______
2. The plan defines the project's purpose.	______	______	______
3. The plan describes the target audience.	______	______	______
4. The plan includes a complete list of tasks required to achieve the goal.	______	______	______
5. The tasks are organized in a step-by-step order.	______	______	______
6. The plan identifies problems and proposes solutions.	______	______	______
7. The plan includes dates for checking on progress toward the goal.	______	______	______
Total	______	______	______

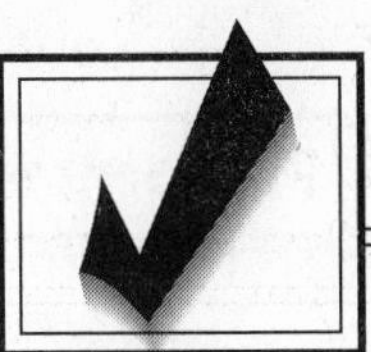